DANIEL HARTWELL  NEILL CAMERON

THE PIRATES OF PANGAEA

BOOK 1

WRITTEN BY

Messrs. Daniel HARTWELL and Neill CAMERON

ILLUSTRATED BY

Mr. Neill CAMERON

COLOURING
ASSISTANCE BY

WITH SPECIAL
THANKS TO

Ms. Abigail

Mr. Benjamin

FIRST PUBLISHED IN GREAT BRITAIN IN 2014 BY
DAVID FICKLING BOOKS,
31 BEAUMONT STREET,
OXFORD, OX1 2NP

TEXT © DANIEL HARTWELL, 2015
ILLUSTRATIONS © NEILL CAMERON, 2015

978-1-910200-08-7

1 3 5 7 9 10 8 6 4 2

DAVID FICKLING BOOKS SUPPORTS THE FOREST STEWARDSHIP COUNCIL (FSC®),
THE LEADING INTERNATIONAL FOREST CERTIFICATION ORGANISATION. ALL OUR TITLES
THAT ARE PRINTED ON GREENPEACE-APPROVED FSC®-CERTIFIED PAPER CARRY THE FSC® LOGO.

MIX
Paper from
responsible sources
FSC
www.fsc.org   FSC® C015140

DAVID FICKLING BOOKS REG. No. 8340307

A CIP CATALOGUE RECORD FOR THIS BOOK IS AVAILABLE FROM THE BRITISH LIBRARY.

PRINTED AND BOUND IN GREAT BRITAIN BY POLESTAR STONES.

THE FELL TYPES ARE DIGITALLY REPRODUCED BY IGINO MARINI. WWW.IGINOMARINI.COM

CONTENTS

Property of
Timothy Kelsey.

CHAPTER ONE

Ambush on Pangaea

SEA OF GREEN

PORT SYLVESTER

Sophie's Journey

SAUROPODA

(Sore - oh- pod - a)

Colloquiallisms: "LONG-NECKS", "LAND LEVIATHANS"
Diet: ~~Omnivorous~~ (?) *Strictly herbivorous.*

(gassy?)

The workhorse of EMPIRE! Now that these titanic CREATURES
have been domesticated, much of the formerly impassable terrain of
the island of PANGAEA has been opened up, allowing the brave souls
riding on their backs to create NEW SETTLEMENTS and trade routes.

Though all bear a certain familial resemblance one to another, there seem
to be several distinct species of sauropod, ranging in weight from twenty
TONS up to a monstrous FIFTY tons in full-grown females.

*definitely
seen
bigger!*

OH!

AHOY THAR, BOSUN WILLIAM!

WHO'S THIS LASS WI' YE?

SOPHIE LASS, THIS HERE'S SNUFFMAN JOHN. IT'S HIS BAG O' TRICKS THAT KEEPS THIS BEASTIE DOCILE.

PLEASED TO MEET YOU.

WELL, MOST PEOPLE ARE TERRIBLY SILLY. SHE'S *BEAUTIFUL*.

WHAT'S HER NAME?

AHOY, SNUFFMAN JOHN!

THIS IS MISS SOPHIE DELACOURT, THE GOVERNOR'S NIECE.

SHE'S OFF TO JOIN HIS LORDSHIP'S 'OUSE'OLD.

YOU'RE A BRAVE ONE. MOST PEOPLE ARE TERRIFIED OF THE LONGNECKS WHEN THEY FIRST SEE 'EM.

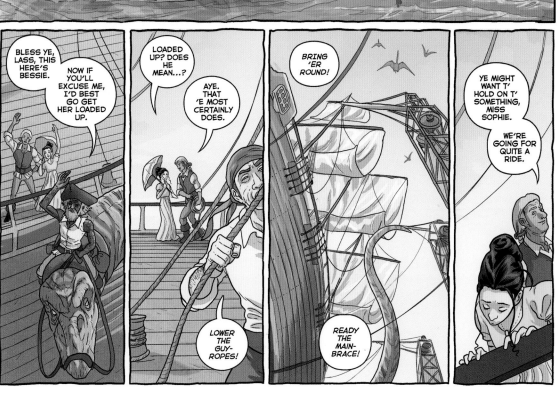

CAREFUL THERE, LASS! IT'D BE MORE'N MY LIFE'S WORTH IF YOU TOOK A TUMBLE INTO THE SEA OF GREEN.

WHAT? IT'S ONLY GRASS

BEGGIN' YER PARDON, MISS SOPHIE, BUT THAT IT AIN'T.

TRUST ME - NOTHING BUT A LONGNECK CAN SET FOOT IN THAT ACCURSED GREEN AND LIVE.

I WAS JUST TRYING TO GET A BETTER LOOK - I THOUGHT I SAW ANOTHER SHIP.

I SHOULDN'T THINK SO. WE'RE THE ONLY INBOUND CRAFT AT PRESENT.

THERE! SEE?

WAIT - NO! IT CAN'T BE...

PIRATES!

GRAUNGHHH

PIRATES?

SEE FOR YERSELF!

GRUBBY LOOKING BAND, AIN'T THEY, MISS SOPHIE?

KA·BOOM!!!

EEEK! THEY'RE SHOOTING AT US!

HA, THEY'LL NEVER HIT US FROM THERE!

KR·KOOW!!!

THEY'VE GOT HEAVY ORDNANCE!

HARD TO PORT, SNUFFMAN JOHN!

AYE, CAPTAIN!

READY CANNONS!

DON'T WORRY, LASS. BESSIE'S FASTER THAN THAT UGLY GREAT MAN O' WAR.

WE'LL SHAKE THOSE BILGE-RATS ONCE WE'RE THROUGH THIS PASS!

YOU HEARD 'IM, LASS.

BUT I WANT TO WATCH!

HEAD BETWEEN THOSE HILLS!

WE'LL USE 'EM FOR COVER.

BOSUN. GET THAT GIRL INSIDE! THIS IS NO PLACE FOR CHILDREN!

AYE, CAP'N!

AND WE'RE OUTRUNNING THEM - YOU SAID SO YOURSELF!

AYE, WELL. WE'RE NOT OUT OF THE WOODS YET.

I'LL STAY OUT OF THE WAY!

THIS ISN'T A GAME, SOPHIE. THOSE ARE DANGEROUS MEN OUT THERE.

STAY IN HERE, LASS, IT'S FOR YER OWN GOOD.

BUT...

CLICK

KA-SHING!

HAVE AT YE!

I'VE GOT TO HELP HIM!

THAT ROPE —

AROUND ITS LEG...

IF I CAN UNFURL THE SAIL...

OOOF! HOLD ON, MASTER BOSUN!

WHAT'S HAPPENING BACK THERE?

UNF — COME ON...

GET THE SNUFFMAN!

BLAM!!

RRRAAAAUGGHH!

AAAIIIEEEEE!!

WHOA!

FWOOOMP!

rawk?

PRRAWKK!

WHOOOOSHH!!

WHUMP!

OWW!

ALL RIGHT, LADS, IT'S TIME TO...

SURRENDER!

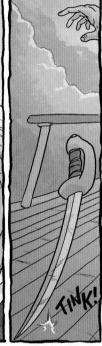

AND LET *THAT* BE A LESSON TO THE REST OF YER!

NOW, WHOEVER DID *THIS*, THEY'RE NEXT!

YOU'LL *ALL* GO OVER ONE AT A TIME UNTIL THEY STEP FORWARD!

I DID IT!

AND YOU ARE IN SO MUCH TROUBLE! MY UNCLE WILL HEAR OF THIS!

AND WHO'S HE? THE GOVERNOR OR SOMETHING?

YES, ACTUALLY!

GOVERNOR SILAS'S NIECE, EH?

I BET HE'LL PAY A PRETTY PENNY TO GET YOU BACK...

CHAPTER TWO

Lost in the Sea of Green

PORT
SYLVES

SEA
OF
GREEN

Our Journey

TYRANT
HILLS

PTEROSAURIA

(*Ter - oh - sore - ee - ya*)

Colloquialisms: *"RAZOR BEAKS", "GREAT-WINGS"*
Diet: Carnivorous

I have encountered many Flying REPTILES in my time on the island.
For many new arrivals to PANGAEA they are often the first native
fauna they see; diving for fish from their cliffside nests. Size seems
to range widely - I have encountered specimens with the wingspan
of a great EAGLE, and others as small as a CHAFFINCH.

Yes
Terrifying!?

Indeed, rumours have reached me of even larger specimens
soaring overhead amongst the INLAND MOUNTAINS. One
imagines how thrilling it must be to ride one of these magnificent
creatures, soaring through the sky with the freedom of a bird!

"thrilling"
indeed!

WAIT... YOU'RE *NOT* ONE OF THEM?

NO, MISS. IN A WAY I SUPPOSE WE'RE BOTH PRISONERS HERE.

I *THOUGHT* YOU WERE A BIT TOO POLITE AND WELL SPOKEN FOR A PIRATE.

I CAME HERE TO WORK FOR A GENTLEMAN CALLED DR SHAW.

HE WAS A MEMBER OF THE ROYAL SOCIETY, HERE TO STUDY THE DINOSAURS.

I WAS HIS ASSISTANT.

HE WAS WORKING ON THE NEXT VOLUME OF THIS BOOK.

INDIGENOUS FAUNA OF THE PANGAEAN LAND-MASS

IT'S INCREDIBLY USEFUL OUT HERE IN THE SEA OF GREEN.

BUT MOSTLY I KEEP IT TO REMIND ME OF HIM.

WE WERE OUT ON A SCIENTIFIC EXPEDITION WHEN BROOKES ATTACKED US.

ONCE HE'D CAPTURED US, HIS FIRST ACT WAS TO SEND DR SHAW OVER THE EDGE. JUST LIKE YOUR CAPTAIN.

THERE WASN'T MUCH LOOT. HE TOOK WHAT SUPPLIES WE HAD, AND ONE MORE THING.

HE DECIDED HE NEEDED A NEW CABIN BOY...

42

WOULD YEH LOOK AT ALL THIS...

OOH!

I'M FAMISHED! LET'S TUCK IN!

WHAT ARE YOU DOING?

IT'S BRONTOSAUR JERKY. WANT SOME?

THERE'S RUM TOO.

MUST BE A SMUGGLER'S HIDEOUT. CAN'T BELIEVE THE LUCK!

ISN'T IT BEAUTIFUL? SUNRISE OVER PANGAEA.

SO PEACEFUL. SO...

RRAAARRRR

WHAT HAPPENED TO THE SMUGGLER?

TYRANT MUST'VE GOT 'IM. WE WERE DAMN LUCKY TO MAKE IT HERE.

AND WHY *ARE* YOU HERE, MISTER JONES?

EH?

YEAH - WHY'D YOU STEAL OUR PTERODACTYL, ANYWAY?

SOPHIE AND I *HAD* TO JUMP SHIP, BUT YOU WERE BROOKES' RIGHT-HAND MAN! WHY LEAVE HIM NOW?

I GOT MY REASONS.

FINE, *DON'T* TELL US.

KELSEY, OVER HERE! I THINK THERE'S A WAY OUT...

THE TYRANT!

IT'S STILL AFTER US...

It can't reach us up here!

But that means we can't get out!

There's nothing we can do. We're *marooned*.

But we've got to get *out* of here!

I've got to get back to civilisation! And Sophie needs to get to her uncle!

Hush up and let a man drink, will yeh?

Hmmm...

We can't stay here forever! What are we going to *do*?

Might as well get some sleep. We ain't goin' anywhere in a hurry.

Rrrgh! You useless *pirate*!

Don't worry. I'm getting an idea...

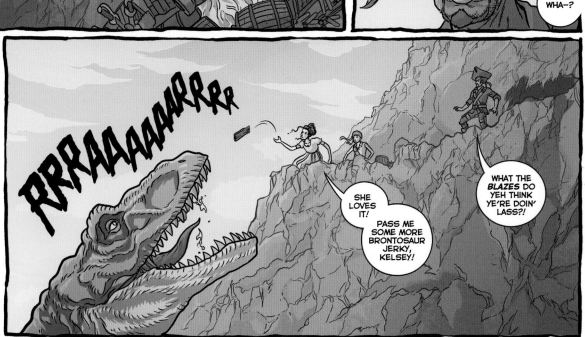

THERE'S A GOOD GIRL...

AMAZING!

HOW'D YOU DO THAT, LASS?

THERE WAS A WOMAN BACK HOME - OLD JEMMY. WHEN WE'D HAVE A PROBLEM WITH THE HORSES WE'D GO TO HER.

SHE WAS ONE OF THE GREAT HORSE WHISPERERS. PEOPLE WOULD COME FROM ALL OVER THE COUNTY TO HAVE HER SOOTHE A TROUBLED HORSE.

AFTER MY PARENTS DIED, SHE HELPED TO LOOK AFTER ME, AND TAUGHT ME A THING OR TWO ABOUT HOW TO CARE FOR ANIMALS.

IT APPEARS IT WORKS ON DINOSAURS TOO.

...I THINK I'M GOING TO CALL HER 'CORNFLOWER'.

...CORNFLOWER?

THIS IS AMAZING! WE CAN USE HER TO GET OFF THIS ROCK!

YES, BUT I'VE GOT NO IDEA WHERE WE ARE, OR HOW TO GET US BACK TO CIVILISATION.

...OH YEAH.

I CAN GET US TO SAFETY.

YEAH, LIKE WE CAN TRUST YOU! YOU'VE ALREADY BETRAYED ONE CAPTAIN.

KELSEY, WE DON'T REALLY HAVE A CHOICE. THERE'S NOWHERE ELSE TO GO...

DON'T YOU WORRY, LASS... YOU CAN TRUST OL' TEN GUN...

CHAPTER
THREE
Secrets of Raptor Rock

GRAVEYARD OF MONSTERS

RAPTOR ROCK

NOTHING TO SEE HERE. SECRET!

GO AWAY!

TYRANT HILLS

Our Journey

DROMAEOSAURIDAE

(*Drom - ay - oh -sore - rid - day*)

Colloquiallisms: "LAND SHARKS", "BELLY RIPPERS"
Diet: Carnivorous ← *Extremely !!!*

These swift two-legged beasts seem to come in a variety of sizes ranging from pigeon to PONY. The smaller varieties are fairly harmless (though I have become acquainted in my time here with many a NINE-FINGERED SAILOR), but the larger ones are quite frankly terrifying. They hunt the PANGAEAN GRASSLANDS in packs, spelling certain doom for any poor soul who sets foot in the cursed "Sea of Green", as that vast insland expanse has come to be known.

Although vicious, they have little INTELLIGENCE, and should in theory be easily ~~OUTWITTED~~ by nimbler creatures.

No! Crafty devils, they are!

GOSH!

THIS HERE'S RAPTOR ROCK. BEST KEPT SECRET IN ALL OF PANGAEA.

I FEEL I HAVE TO ASK YOU AGAIN MR JONES...

HOW IS A LIVE VOLCANO, THAT IS ALSO FILLED WITH PIRATES 'SAFE'?

RELAX, THEY KNOW ME HERE.

TEN GUN! HOW'D YOU WIND UP WITH A TYRANT?

YEH CAN TETHER YER BEAST UP HERE, LASS.

HER *NAME* IS CORNFLOWER.

PLEASE TAKE GOOD CARE OF HER...

ULP!

TEN GUN JONES!

I TRUST YOU DIDN'T RETURN EMPTY HANDED?

AYE, CAPTAIN FORD. I'VE GOT IT WITH ME.

EXCELLENT, ME BOY! COME JOIN THE LADS IN THE CUTLASS AND CLAW.

BY THE WAY, WHERE'D THESE WHIPPER-SNAPPERS COME FROM?

HE STOLE OUR RIDE WHEN WE WERE TRYING TO ESCAPE FROM BROOKES!

THEY STOWED AWAY WHEN I WAS ESCAPING FROM BROOKES.

HEY!

HAH! C'MON IN AND YOU CAN TELL ME ALL ABOUT IT.

THE LADS ARE ALL SUPPING ON RIB.

DON'T YOU MEAN 'RIBS'?

NO, LASS...

...I DON'T THINK ANYONE COULD EAT MORE THAN ONE OF THESE!

BRONTO-SAUR RIB!

AND ORNITHOMIMUS DRUMSTICKS!

CAPTAIN FORD? WOULD YOU BE ABLE TO GIVE ME SOME DIRECTIONS SO I CAN GET BACK TO CIVILISATION?

I COULD.

BUT I WON'T.

Y'SEE, MISSY, THIS PLACE 'ERE IS THE BEST KEPT SECRET IN ALL PANGAEA, AND I AIM TO KEEP IT THAT WAY!

WELCOME TO RAPTOR ROCK... YOU'LL NEVER LEAVE!

WHAT DO YOU MEAN?!

CAN'T HAVE YOU BLABBIN' OUR SECRETS TO THE AUTHORITIES, NOW, CAN I?

YOU CAN'T DO THIS TO ME! I SIMPLY MUST GET TO FORT WILLIAM TO SEE MY UNCLE!

DO YOU KNOW WHO I AM?

SHUT IT, YOU!

I DON'T CARE WHO YOU ARE, AND NEITHER DOES ANYONE ELSE!

SORRY 'BOUT THAT, CAPTAIN.

THESE KIDS ARE AWFUL MOUTHY.

NOT A PROBLEM, TEN GUN... GRAB YOURSELF A FLASK OF ALE.

WHY, I'M GOING TO GIVE THAT ROTTEN PIRATE A PIECE OF MY MIND!

WHY? HE JUST SAVED YOU!

IF FORD FOUND OUT THAT YOU'RE THE GOVERNOR'S NIECE HE'D JUST TRY TO RANSOM YOU, SAME AS BROOKES DID.

HUH - SURPRISED HE CARED.

OH... I SEE...

NOW TO BUSINESS, TEN GUN. LET'S SEE MY MAP.

NEARLY THERE...

WHOA!

EEEK!

GOT YOU!

DON'T WORRY, CHILD.

YOU SAFE NOW.

YOU NEED BE CAREFUL, GIRL. GERTRUDE HERE'S A BIT SPOOKED, BEIN' IN THIS PLACE OF THE DEAD.

COME, SIT WITH ME A WHILE.

ALL RIGHT...

WHERE ARE YOU FROM, MR TAK?

I OF THE BWO IWAKIA. WE IWAKIANS LIVE IN THIS LAND BEFORE YOU PEOPLE COME.

REALLY? GOSH! WHY DIDN'T YOU ALL GET EATEN?

HA!

WE USE THE SNUFF, GIRL. WE TEACH IT TO YOU. THAT'S WHY WE'RE HERE NOW.

SAW YOU RIDE IN ON THAT TYRANT.

OH THAT, I JUST DID WHAT HAD TO BE DONE TO GET US OUT OF THERE.

NOT MANY PEOPLE COULD DO THAT, GIRL. YOU SPECIAL.

WHAT DO YOU THINK OF CAPTAIN FORD?

HE NOT AN EVIL MAN, BUT HE GOT THE GOLD LUST PRETTY BAD.

THIS GOLDEN SKULL HE AFTER... IT BELONG TO THE KRON IWAKIA. THEY NOT JUST LET HIM TAKE IT.

YOU SEE SOON. WE HERE!

LAND HO!

CHAPTER FOUR
Quest for the Golden Skull

THE FORBIDDEN ISLE

Our Journey

GRAVEYARD OF MONSTERS

TYRANNOSAURIDAE

(Ty - ran - oh - sore - ih - day)

Colloquialisms: *"TYRANTS"*
Diet: Carnivorous

— at least 15

9

With some species reaching a terrifying **TEN FEET** in height, and
weighing upwards of **SEVEN TONS** , these are the largest and
by far the most **FEARSOME** land-based Predatory creatures I
have encountered in my travels across **PANGAEA**. I have observed
(from a safe distance) a **WIDE VARIATION** in colours and
markings, though I have as yet been unable to discern whether
this is a matter of natural pigmentation or the work
of the native **IWAKIAN PEOPLE**.

Very few who have directly encountered a **TYRANT** have survived
to tell their tale. These are truly terrifying creatures, reminscent of
the very **DEMONS** of **HELL ITSELF**.

Too right!

Nonsense!
Cornflower is very
sweet-tempered!

RIGHT, LADS!

UNLOAD THE VICTUALS, YOU LOLLYGAGGING SWAB-HANDS!

ALL RIGHT! TEN GUN, TAK, PETERSEN, MATTHEWS AND JOSEPH, YOU'RE WITH ME - LET'S FIND THIS HERE SKULL!

LEGEND HAS IT THAT IT CAN MAKE ITS' OWNER *INVINCIBLE IN BATTLE.* WE SELL IT, IT'LL KEEP US IN RUM FOR *MONTHS!*

WHEN DO WE LEAVE?

YOU AIN'T GOIN' NOWHERE. 'TIS NO PLACE FOR INEXPERIENCED CHILDREN.

INEXPERIENCED?! SO FAR I'VE ESCAPED FROM PIRATES, FLOWN ON A RAZORBEAK, RUN BLIND THROUGH THE SEA OF GREEN, AND PERSONALLY TRAINED A TYRANT!

SHE HAS A POINT.

... WELL, YOU'VE GOT ME THERE.

C'MON, BUT YOU'D BETTER KEEP UP.

THANK YOU, CAPTAIN!

DON'T THANK ME, YOU SOUND LIKE FAR TOO MUCH TROUBLE TO LEAVE UNSUPERVISED. I'LL HAVE MY EYE ON YOU.

I'LL STAY HERE.

NO ONE ASKED YOU.

BET IT'S NOT THAT IMPRESSIVE ANYWAY.

"...GET BACK TO THE SHIP WHILE WE STILL CAN!"

SHIP AHOY!

WHAT COLOURS THEY FLYIN'?

CAN'T TELL...

MUST BE THE NAVY. NO ONE ELSE'D BE THIS FAR OUT.

HEADING?

SOUTH, SOUTH EAST. THEY'LL GO RIGHT PAST US!

THEY CAN'T SEE US THROUGH THE TREE LINE. WE SHOULD BE SAFE ENOUGH.

STILL, THOUGH... IF THEY CHANGE HEADING...

YOU, BOY!

GO FETCH UP THE GUNPOWDER. WE MIGHT HAVE A FIGHT ON OUR HANDS!

THE NAVY! I'VE GOT TO SIGNAL THEM SOMEHOW!

BOOM!!

THE NAVY! THEY'VE *FOUND* US!

YEH LITTLE BRAT, YOU'VE BROUGHT THE REDCOATS DOWN ON US...

THAT'S NOT THE NAVY! IT'S...

CAPTAIN BROOKES!

BOOM!

KELSEY, EVER SINCE I ARRIVED HERE ALL I'VE *DONE* IS RUN AWAY FROM THINGS.

SO I'M GETTING RATHER GOOD AT IT. COME ON!

THERE SHE IS! THE ONE WHO HUNG MY LANDSHARK FROM THE YARD ARM!

AND SHE STOLE MY RAZORBEAK!

GET HER!

THEY'RE AFTER US!

QUICK - INTO THE TREES! WE'LL LOSE THEM!

KRA-
BOOM!

POW!

SO...?

OH NO!

DEAD END!

THEY'RE TRAPPED - WE'VE GOT 'EM NOW!

YOU BRATS HAVE HAD THIS COMING FOR A LONG TIME!

WE'RE DOOMED!

CLOSE YOUR EYES, KELSEY.

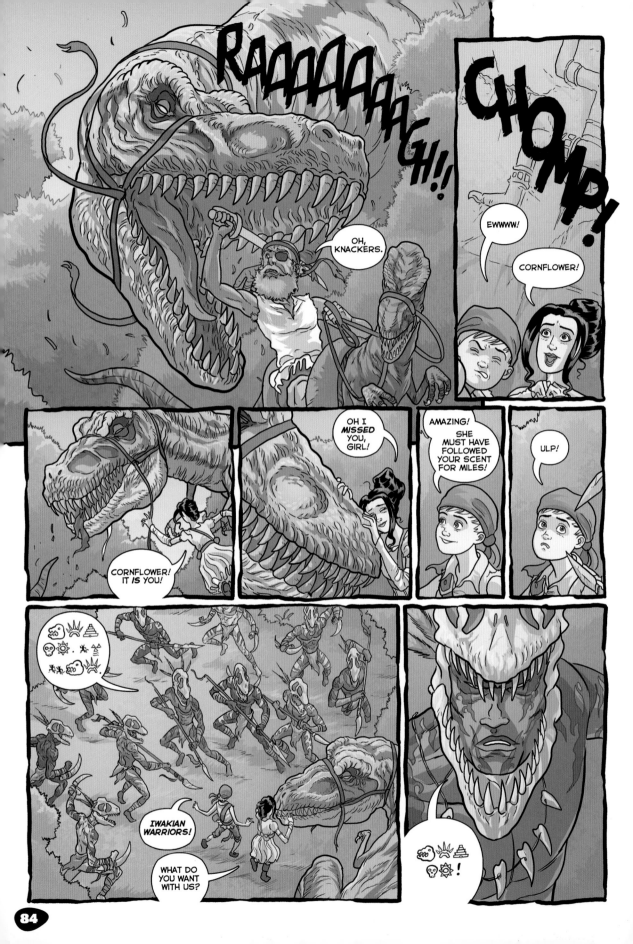

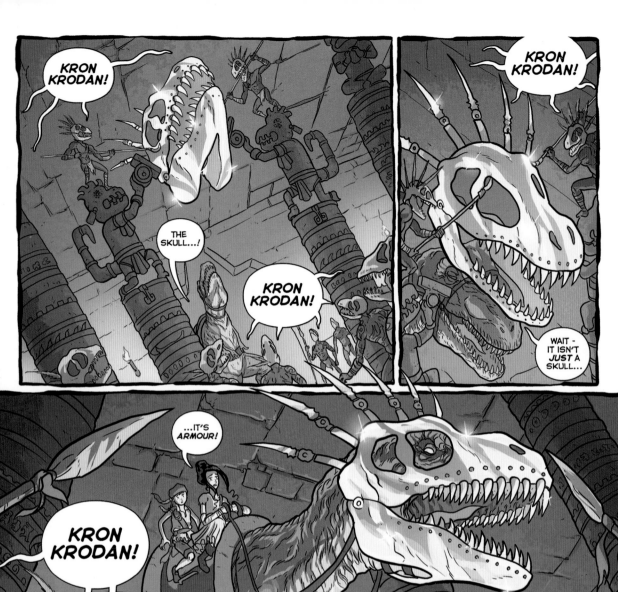

DIE, YOU MEDDLIN' BRAT!

NOT IF I CAN HELP IT!

SWISSSSSH!

CHONK!

INTO THE SEA OF GREEN WITH YOU!

THE LAND-SHARKS'LL DINE WELL TONIGHT...

SOPHIE! NO!

NOTHING YOU CAN DO ABOUT IT, TEN GUN! YOU'RE ALL OUT OF GUNS!

REAARRRGH

AND DON'T THINK YOUR LITTLE FRIEND'LL SAVE YOU EITHER!

HOW DO I STEER THIS THING? AAAAAH!

OVER YOU GO!